THE SELFISH CRAB

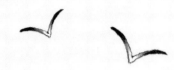

OXFORD
UNIVERSITY PRESS

Great Clarendon Street, Oxford OX2 6DP
Oxford University Press is a department of the University of Oxford.
It furthers the University's objective of excellence in research, scholarship,
and education by publishing worldwide. Oxford is a registered trade mark
of Oxford University Press in the UK and in certain other countries

Database right Oxford University Press (maker)

First published in 2023

British Library Cataloguing in Publication Data

Data available

ISBN: 978-0-19-277781-2

1 3 5 7 9 10 8 6 4 2

Printed in China

Paper used in the production of this book is a natural,
recyclable product made from wood grown in sustainable forests.
The manufacturing process conforms to the environmental
regulations of the country of origin.

For my parents

ANYA GLAZER

THE SELFISH CRAB

OXFORD
UNIVERSITY PRESS

On a palm-fringed island, lived a scuttle of hermit crabs. The crabs lived in borrowed shells of every size and shape.

Margot

Patty

Alphonso

Gigi

Barnabus

And one crab knew he had the best shell of all ...

Otto

Ernestine

Gladys

Franklin

Claude was not the most humble of hermit crabs.

But how could he be . . .

. . . when his shell was so magnificent?

Now the thing about hermit crabs is that eventually they outgrow their shells.

So they're on the lookout for empty shells that wash ashore.

When this happens, all of the crabs gather together.

They line up in size order, so that one by one they can move
into the next biggest shell.

And there was nothing
the others could do to
make him change his mind.

The crabs did their best to keep going, but Claude had caused such a muddle that afterwards things just weren't quite right.

But for Claude, life was great.

What did it matter if he had caused a bit of a fuss, or if the other hermit crabs were snubbing him?

Or if little Alphonso's new shell was far too big . . .

as long as he still had his own beautiful shell?

(Which definitely wasn't starting to feel a bit tight now.)

'Much quieter without the others,' said Alphonso.

'Oh yes, it's very peaceful,' said Claude.
'Just us and the dolphins and the birds.'

'Birds?' said Alphonso.

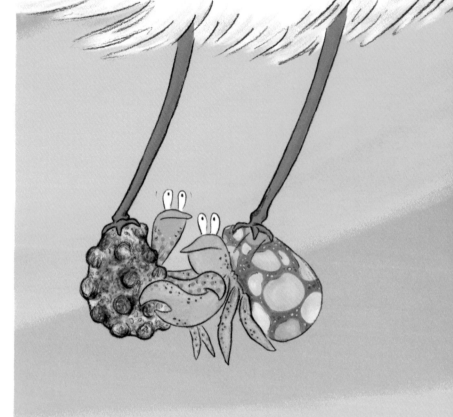

Claude wriggled out to reach
Alphonso – then found he was stuck.

His shell was too tight.

He could not fit back in!

'What now?' said Claude.

'I have an idea,' said Alphonso.
'Just don't let go!'

And  PINCH

They were free!

Free and plummeting
down,
    down,
        down
            until…

they were welcomed with a soft landing.

'Thank you all for catching us,' said Claude. 'And if it wasn't for Alphonso we would never have escaped . . .

I'm sorry for causing such trouble.'

I think I'm ready to swap shells now.

And so the hermit crabs prepared once more to exchange shells.

and especially Gladys.

Just LOOK at how fabulously this new shell suits me.

ALL ABOUT HERMIT CRABS

Hermit crabs are part of the **crustacean** family. The front part of their bodies is covered with a hard outer layer called an **exoskeleton**, but their bellies (or **abdomen**) are soft and must be protected by crawling into empty seashells. As the hermit crab grows it moves into bigger shells. There are over 800 species of hermit crab, which can be found both on land and in the sea. Even though they are called hermit crabs, they are more closely related to some lobsters than true crabs—and, far from living alone, they can sometimes be found in groups of a hundred or more and pile up together when they sleep!

A LAND HERMIT CRAB

Hermit crabs have five pairs of legs. The fourth and fifth pair are inside the shell, along with their abdomen which hooks around the shell.

Some species have a bigger right pincer than left, which they use to cover the opening to their shell when they are in danger.

Land hermit crabs live in tropical areas. They still need access to water to keep their gills damp. Crabs use gills for breathing.

A MARINE HERMIT CRAB

Some crabs carry sea anemones, which they take with them as they move to bigger shells. By travelling with a hermit crab the anemone can find a wider supply of food and, in return, its stinging tentacles help protect the hermit crab from attack.

Marine hermit crabs spend most of their lives underwater. Some stay around rock pools and shallows, while others live deep in the ocean.

What makes a good shell?

A good shell will keep a crab safe, it should be:

Not too small, and not too big.

The right size to hide in completely.

Strong, and ideally not damaged.

And stay out!

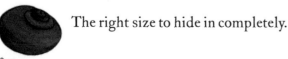

Hermit crabs are found all around the world ...

In the UK, tiny hermit crabs measuring 1–4cm live in rock pools all along the coast.

Caribbean hermit crabs hide inland under tree roots. They eat fruit, soft wood and even iguana poo.

Coconut crabs are found in the Pacific and Indian oceans. Young crabs need to find shells to protect their bodies before their exoskeletons harden. Adults grow up to 1m long, can crack open coconuts with their pincers and have been known to hunt birds!

The great hermit crab shell swap

Hermit crabs really do sometimes swap shells in size order. Hermit crabs will inspect a new empty shell and if it is not right for them, they will wait beside it. More crabs will emerge and inspect the shell in turn, and arrange themselves in a line as they wait for the right-sized hermit crab to come along.

Once the crab that best matches the size of the shell has arrived, the shell exchange can begin. As it's dangerous for hermit crabs to stay out of their shells, it all happens very quickly! When all goes according to plan, it looks something like this . . .

Threats to hermit crabs

Hermit crabs are hunted by **predators** including fish, larger crabs and some birds. They are also affected by **climate change** and pollution. When plastic litter ends up on their beaches, hermit crabs may get confused. They can mistake it for food or even sometimes replacement shells, which can be very harmful—for example causing the crabs to become trapped.

The Seashore Code

If you go to the beach, you can explore the rock pools and look for hermit crabs for yourself. Be sure to follow the Seashore Code: treat all wildlife with care and handle creatures as little as possible, always put overturned rocks back carefully as you found them, take your rubbish home with you or put it in the bin, and keep safe on the seashore.